Original title: Here Comes the April Fool!

You're barking up the wrong tree, Snoopy!

by Charles M. Schulz

SCHOLASTIC BOOK SERVICES

NEW YORK • TORONTO • LONDON • AUCKLAND • SYDNEY • TOKYO

ISBN: 0-590-32261-3

12 11 10 9 8 7 6 5 4 3 2 1   11   1 2 3 4 5 6/8

Printed in the U.S.A.   11

You're barking up the wrong tree, Snoopy!

BEEP!

HERE'S THE WORLD WAR I FLYING ACE SITTING IN A SMALL CAFE IN FRANCE

HE IS LONELY... HE IS DEPRESSED

HE REALIZES THAT HIS GIRL BACK HOME DOESN'T LOVE HIM ANY MORE..EVEN THOUGH SHE JUST SENT HIM A BOX OF COOKIES...

THEY'RE ALL FILLED WITH COCONUT!

BLEAH!

AAK!

HERE'S THE WORLD WAR I FLYING ACE ZOOMING THROUGH THE AIR IN HIS SOPWITH CAMEL...

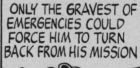

ONLY THE GRAVEST OF EMERGENCIES COULD FORCE HIM TO TURN BACK FROM HIS MISSION

SUPPERTIME!

IT'S THE RED BARON! HE'S ON MY TAIL!

HERE'S WHERE ALL MY MONTHS OF TRAINING WILL COME TO USE...

THE FIRST THING THEY TAUGHT US WAS TO SEEK COVER IN THE CLOUDS

IN TRAINING WE HAD BIGGER CLOUDS

HERE'S THE WORLD WAR I FLYING ACE WALKING ALONG A COUNTRY ROAD IN FRANCE...

HE NOTICES A BEAUTIFUL YOUNG GIRL APPROACHING FROM THE OPPOSITE DIRECTION...HE SPEAKS..

BONJOUR, SWEETIE!

SHE IS NOT IMPRESSED BY HIS FLUENT FRENCH

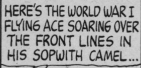

HERE'S THE WORLD WAR I FLYING ACE BEING CHASED BY THE RED BARON...

HE HATES ME!

EVERYONE ASKS HOW I KNOW HE HATES ME...

I CAN TELL!

SCHULZ

HERE'S THE WORLD WAR I FLYING ACE STROLLING DOWN A COUNTRY ROAD...ONCE AGAIN HE SEES THE CHARMING FRENCH LASS..

QUICKLY HE CONSULTS HIS PHRASE BOOK... "I AM HAPPY TO MEET YOU"

ENCHANTÉ DE FAIRE VOTRE CONNAISSANCE

彬 SIGH 彬

SCHULZ

"MAY I SEE YOU THIS EVENING? POURRAI-JE VOUS VOIR CE SOIR?"

" I THINK YOU ARE BEAUTIFUL...JE VOUS TROUVE TRÈS JOLIE"

I LOVE YOU! JE VOUS AIME!

"WHERE IS THE MUSEUM? OÙ EST LE MUSÉE?"

EVERY DAY WHEN I WALK TO SCHOOL, I MEET THIS STRANGE CREATURE...

HE WEARS GOGGLES AND A WHITE SCARF

THAT'S MY BROTHER'S DOG...HE'S WEIRD...

YOUR BROTHER OR HIS DOG?

BOTH!

"GOOD EVENING, MISS...
BONSOIR, MADEMOISELLE"

"MAY I INVITE YOU TO
DANCE? PUIS-JE VOUS
INVITER À DANSER?
YOU DANCE VERY WELL..
VOUS DANSEZ TRÈS BIEN"

BONSOIR, MONSIEUR

RATS! I SWALLOWED
MY PHRASE BOOK!

HERE'S THE WORLD WAR I
FLYING ACE SITTING IN A
LITTLE CAFE...ONCE AGAIN
HE IS DEPRESSED...

HIS LEAVE IS OVER,
AND HE HAS FAILED
TO MEET THE CHARMING
FRENCH LASS...

HE DECIDES TO FORGET
HER BY DRINKING ROOT
BEER...GARÇON! ANOTHER
ROUND, S'IL VOUS PLAÎT!

UNFORTUNATELY, IT'S VERY
HARD TO FORGET ANYONE
BY DRINKING ROOT BEER!

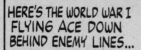

ISN'T THIS A BEAUTIFUL VALENTINE? IT SAYS, "I LOVE YOU...I LOVE YOU"

I THINK I'LL GIVE IT TO THE LITTLE RED-HAIRED GIRL

SHE'LL PROBABLY LAUGH RIGHT IN YOUR FACE

AT LEAST I'D BE NEAR HER!

ANY VALENTINES IN THERE?

ANY VALENTINES IN THERE?

NOTHING ECHOES LIKE AN EMPTY MAILBOX

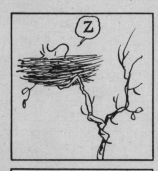
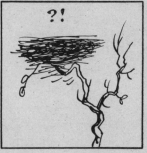

888888'S

I'M WRITING A STORY ABOUT THE "EIGHT WHO ATE EIGHTS"

SEE? IT SAYS, "EIGHT ATE EIGHT HUNDRED AND EIGHTY-EIGHT EIGHTS"

WHAT DO YOU THINK?

I 'ATE TO TELL YOU!

NO, MA'AM..I DON'T KNOW THE ANSWER

I WAS JUST SIGNALING FOR A FAIR CATCH!

YOU'RE LUCKY, DO YOU KNOW THAT, BIRD? YOU'RE LUCKY BECAUSE YOU DON'T HAVE TO STUDY MATH!

YOU DON'T HAVE TO KNOW ABOUT RATIONALIZING THE DENOMINATOR AND DUMB THINGS LIKE THAT

YOU'RE REALLY LUCKY

$$\frac{7\sqrt{2}}{\sqrt{6}} \cdot \frac{\sqrt{6}}{\sqrt{6}} = \frac{7\sqrt{2 \cdot 3}}{6} = \frac{7}{3}\sqrt{3}$$

YOU KNOW WHAT I THINK YOU HAVE, SIR? YOU HAVE "MATH ANXIETY"

IF I ASKED YOU HOW MANY WAYS THAT NINE BOOKS COULD BE ARRANGED ON A SHELF, WHAT WOULD BE YOUR FIRST REACTION?

AAUGHH!

SEE? YOU HAVE "MATH ANXIETY"

"HOW MANY ANGELS CAN STAND ON THE HEAD OF A PIN?"

THIS MUST BE KIND OF A PHILOSOPHICAL QUESTION, HUH, MA'AM?

THE HEAD OF A PIN, HUH? BOY, THAT'S A HARD ONE...

HOW ABOUT A PAPER CLIP?

GET THIS, CHUCK...SHE ASKS US HOW MANY ANGELS CAN STAND ON THE HEAD OF A PIN!

WHAT KIND OF A QUESTION IS THAT, CHUCK? HOW CAN YOU ANSWER SOMETHING LIKE THAT?

YOU CAN'T, PATTY...IT'S AN OLD THEOLOGICAL PROBLEM...THERE REALLY IS NO ANSWER...

THAT'S TOO BAD... I PUT DOWN, "EIGHT, IF THEY'RE SKINNY, AND FOUR IF THEY'RE FAT!"

YOU CAN'T SAY HOW MANY ANGELS CAN STAND ON THE HEAD OF A PIN, SIR... THERE IS NO ANSWER!

WELL, THAT'S JUST GREAT, MARCIE! IF I TRY TO ANSWER A QUESTION, I'M WRONG!

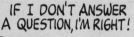

IF I DON'T ANSWER A QUESTION, I'M RIGHT!

THAT'S EDUCATION, SIR!

SORRY ABOUT MY MATH PAPER, MA'AM

ON MY WAY TO SCHOOL THIS MORNING, I SORT OF DROPPED IT IN THE MUD

MAYBE YOU CAN KIND OF BRUSH IT OFF A BIT WITH YOUR SLEEVE.. WANNA TRY IT?

I GUESS NOT

WHAT'S THIS?

IT'S A BOOK ON HANDWRITING AND LETTERING

" AFTER PRACTICING THE CORRECT HAND MOVEMENTS WITH A PENCIL, YOU ARE NOW READY FOR PEN AND INK "

" AS AN AID TO SPEED, YOU WILL NOTE THAT SOME LETTERS ARE JOINED OR LINKED TOGETHER "

" DURING PRACTICE, HOWEVER, IT IS BEST NOT TO TRY TO LINK UP CERTAIN LETTERS... "

I THINK YOU LINKED THEM UP!

I'VE BEEN WORRIED ABOUT THIS FOR A LONG TIME

LET ME ASK YOU SOMETHING...

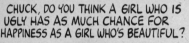

CHUCK, DO YOU THINK A GIRL WHO IS UGLY HAS AS MUCH CHANCE FOR HAPPINESS AS A GIRL WHO'S BEAUTIFUL?

OF COURSE! FOR ONE THING, YOU HAVE A NICE PERSONALITY, AND...

WHAT MAKES YOU THINK I WAS TALKING ABOUT MYSELF, CHUCK?

TRAPPED YOU, DIDN'T I, CHUCK?

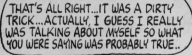

THAT'S ALL RIGHT...IT WAS A DIRTY TRICK...ACTUALLY, I GUESS I REALLY WAS TALKING ABOUT MYSELF SO WHAT YOU WERE SAYING WAS PROBABLY TRUE..

BUT WHAT MADE YOU THINK I WAS TALKING ABOUT MYSELF, CHUCK?

✳SIGH✳

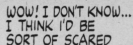

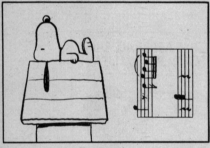

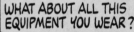

HEY, MANAGER, HOW ARE THE ADVANCE TICKET SALES GOING?

WE SOLD ONE TICKET TO MY GRANDMOTHER

I SUPPOSE YOU'RE GOING TO PUT THAT IN YOUR COLUMN

WHY NOT?

" TICKET SALES ARE WAY UP OVER LAST YEAR "

HEY, YOU STUPID BEAGLE, I'M DOING INTERVIEWS FOR OUR SCHOOL PAPER...

HOW ABOUT A GOOD QUOTE FOR OUR READERS?

BLEAH!

" HE SAID HE EXPECTS TO HAVE ONE OF HIS BEST SEASONS EVER "

"THIS REPORTER HAS NEVER INTERVIEWED A WORSE BASEBALL TEAM"

" THE MANAGER IS INEPT AND THE PLAYERS ARE HOPELESS "

"WE WILL SAY, HOWEVER, THAT THE CATCHER IS KIND OF CUTE, AND THE RIGHT FIELDER, WHO HAS DARK HAIR, IS VERY BEAUTIFUL "

GOOD ARTICLE, HUH ?

POW!

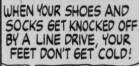

NOW I KNOW WHY WE PLAY BASEBALL IN THE SUMMER...

WHEN YOUR SHOES AND SOCKS GET KNOCKED OFF BY A LINE DRIVE, YOUR FEET DON'T GET COLD!

HEY, MANAGER, IF IT'S NIGHTTIME, HOW COME THE GAME HASN'T BEEN CALLED OFF?

IT ISN'T NIGHTTIME... YOU JUST HAVE A BLANKET OVER YOUR HEAD

OH, REALLY?

WE'RE NUMBER ONE! WE'RE NUMBER ONE!

LOST AGAIN! RATS!!

LOSING ALL THESE GAMES IS DRIVING ME CRAZY!

I WISH I COULD LEARN TO NOT LET IT BOTHER ME..LIKE SOME PEOPLE I KNOW...

WE'RE NUMBER ONE! WE'RE NUMBER ONE!

WHAT'S THAT YOU'RE WEARING AROUND YOUR NECK, CHARLIE BROWN?

IT'S A MEDICAL TAG...LOTS OF PEOPLE WEAR THEM...

WHAT DOES IT SAY?

"INSECURE"

I GUESS IT'S WRONG ALWAYS TO BE WORRYING ABOUT TOMORROW

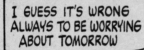

MAYBE WE SHOULD THINK ONLY ABOUT TODAY...

NO, THAT'S GIVING UP...

I'M STILL HOPING THAT YESTERDAY WILL GET BETTER

 I'VE BEEN WATCHING YOU WHEN YOU'RE GETTING READY TO SERVE

 ARE YOU SUPERSTITIOUS?

 I NOTICE THAT YOU NEVER STEP ON THE BASELINE...

 I DON'T WANT TO OFFEND IT

 TOURNAMENT TIME AGAIN, HUH?

 I HEAR YOU'RE PLAYING IN THE THIRTY-FIVES...

 YOU'RE NOT THIRTY-FIVE YEARS OLD

 YEARS? I THOUGHT THEY MEANT INCHES!

IT'S YOUR TURN.. ROLL THE DICE!

WHAT IF ROLLING THESE DICE LEADS ME TO A LIFE OF GAMBLING?

WHAT IF I CAN'T STOP? WHAT IF I BECOME A COMPULSIVE GAMBLER? WHAT IF I...

ROLLING DICE CAN RUIN YOU...SO CAN **NOT** ROLLING DICE!

THERE...I MOVED FIVE SQUARES..NOW, IT'S YOUR TURN...ROLL THE DICE!

IN THE TWENTY-EIGHTH CHAPTER OF EXODUS, IT TELLS OF 'URIM AND THUMMIM'.. SOME SCHOLARS SAY THESE WERE SMALL STONES LIKE DICE

THESE DICE WERE USED TO OBTAIN THE WILL OF GOD WHEN DECISIONS HAD TO BE MADE, AND...

ROLL THE DICE!

THAT'S A GOOD DECISION

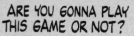

LET ME SEE THAT BOOK! WHAT IS IT?

PHOOEY! I WOULDN'T READ THIS FOR ANYTHING!

NOT IN A MILLION YEARS! FORGET IT! NO WAY!!

LUCY HAS NO TROUBLE JUDGING A BOOK BY ITS COVER!

THE YEARS ARE GOING BY FAST

WILL YOU LOVE ME WHEN I'M OLD AND GRAY?

IF I DON'T LOVE YOU NOW, WHY SHOULD I LOVE YOU THEN?

BECAUSE I'LL BE A SWEET OLD LADY!

WE COULD STILL RUN INTO SOME BAD WEATHER THIS TIME OF YEAR

I THINK YOU SHOULD BE WELL PREPARED LIKE I AM...

TAKE ALONG EXTRA SOCKS, FOOD, DRINK, KNIFE, FORK, SPOON.. ANYTHING YOU CAN THINK OF...

THERE'S NO EXCUSE FOR NOT BEING PROPERLY PREPARED

UH HUH...WELL, MAYBE YOU COULD LEAVE OUT THE FORK AND SPOON...

SCHULZ

A HIKE THROUGH THE WOODS IN THE SPRING CAN BE A JOY AND AN INSPIRATION...

IT CAN REVIVE YOUR SPIRITS, AND IT CAN..

..GET YOU INTO MORE TROUBLE THAN YOU EVER DREAMED OF IN YOUR WHOLE STUPID LIFE!

FINE BUNCH OF BEAGLE SCOUTS YOU GUYS ARE!

YOU SPOT FOUR CHICKS, AND YOU RUN OFF AND LEAVE ME!

YOU ALL FORGOT YOUR BEAGLE SCOUT OATH, "DON'T CUT OUT ON A FRIEND"

INCIDENTALLY, DID YOU HAVE A GOOD TIME?

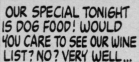

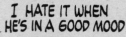

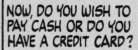

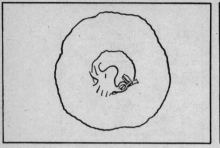

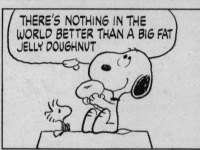

WHAT ARE YOU DOING HERE? YOU'RE SUPPOSED TO BE OUT SOMEWHERE SITTING ON A BRANCH CHIRPING

THAT'S YOUR JOB...PEOPLE EXPECT TO HEAR BIRDS CHIRPING WHEN THEY WAKE UP IN THE MORNING...

CHIRP!

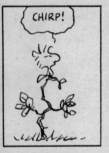

YOU ONLY CHIRPED ONCE...YOU CAN'T BRIGHTEN SOMEONE'S DAY WITH ONE CHIRP!

CHIRP CHIRP
CHIRP CHIRP
CHIRP CHIRP

THERE, NOW! DIDN'T THAT GIVE YOU A FEELING OF REAL SATISFACTION?

THE BAD NEWS IS YOU'RE SUPPOSED TO DO THAT EVERY MORNING FOR THE REST OF YOUR LIFE!

KLUNK

TRUE OR FALSE? I SAY, TRUE! YES! ABSOLUTELY TRUE!

THIS IS ALSO TRUE! EVERYTHING IS TRUE! NOTHING IS FALSE!

THE WHOLE WORLD IS TRUE! WE'RE ALL TRUE! TRUE! TRUE! TRUE!

YOU WOULDN'T CRUSH AN OPTIMIST WITH A 'D-MINUS,' WOULD YOU, MA'AM?

HOW CAN YOU PIG-OUT ON ALL THAT JUNK FOOD EVERY DAY, SIR?

LIFE IS MORE THAN CARROT STICKS, MARCIE

I'LL BET YOU'VE NEVER EVEN TRIED ONE, SIR

WHAT IS A STOMACH THAT'S EXPECTING A CHOCOLATE BAR GOING TO SAY WHEN IT GETS A CARROT STICK?

EXPLAIN TO IT THAT YOU'RE ALL PART OF THE SAME TEAM, SIR...IT'LL APPRECIATE BEING INVOLVED...

WHEN WE GET TO HIGH SCHOOL, I'M HOPING THAT WE'LL HAVE LOCKERS NEXT TO EACH OTHER

THAT WOULD BE AN ODD COMBINATION! HA HA HA HA HA!!

GET IT? LOCKERS HAVE COMBINATION LOCKS! AN ODD COMBINATION! GET IT?

MUSICIANS SHOULD NEVER TRY TO BE FUNNY

YOU NEVER CALL ME "HONEY BUTTER"

IF YOU CALLED ME "HONEY BUTTER," I'D PROBABLY TINGLE ALL OVER...

FORGET IT

SO MUCH FOR TINGLING!

WHERE'S LUCY?

SHE'S LYING IN HER BEAN BAG SULKING

THEN I WON'T BOTHER HER...

I KNOW BETTER THAN TO DISTURB A GOOD SULK

SMART

WHO IS THAT?

THAT'S BLACKJACK SNOOPY, THE WORLD FAMOUS RIVER BOAT GAMBLER...

IS HE FAMOUS BECAUSE HE'S SUCH A GOOD CARD PLAYER?

NO, BECAUSE I HAVE TWO MUSTACHES!

WHAT ARE YOU PLANTING TODAY?

BRUSSELS SPROUTS

IS THIS A GOOD TIME OF YEAR TO PLANT BRUSSELS SPROUTS?

WHO CARES?

BRUSSELS SPROUTS NEVER KNOW WHAT'S GOING ON!

WE GARDENERS ARE ALWAYS READING BOOKS AND PAMPHLETS

HAVE YOU EVER STUDIED CROP ROTATION?

OF COURSE

THAT'S WHERE YOUR TOMATOES DIE ONE YEAR AND YOUR RADISHES DIE THE NEXT YEAR!

BEANS ARE EASY TO GROW

BUT WHILE THEY'RE GROWING, YOU HAVE TO WAIT FOR THEM IN A SPECIAL PLACE

WHERE'S THAT?

IN YOUR BEAN BAG!

HEY! MY BLANKET!

I NEED IT!

WHAT IF WE HAVE A LATE FREEZE TONIGHT?

I NEED YOUR BLANKET TO COVER MY PLANTS

THIS IS THE FIRST TIME IN MY LIFE I'VE EVER SAT UP ALL NIGHT WITH A PARSNIP...

OFF TO MARKET?

WOW! THAT MUST BE EXCITING FOR A NEW FARMER LIKE YOURSELF

GOOD LUCK!

ACTUALLY, HE SHOULDN'T HAVE ANY TROUBLE SELLING ONE RADISH...

SCHULZ

HERE COMES WOODSTOCK BACK FROM THE FARMER'S MARKET

WELL, HOW DID IT GO?

YOU SOLD YOUR RADISH? WOW! THAT'S GREAT!

$

NOW YOU CAN BUY SOME MORE SEED, AND RAISE ANOTHER RADISH!

SCHULZ

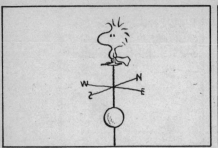

YOU LOOK EXHAUSTED! RUNNING A FARM IS HARD WORK

WELL, OKAY...

I DON'T MIND HELPING OUT ON A FRIEND'S FARM ONCE IN A WHILE...

BUT I HATE BEING THE SCARECROW!

I'VE BEEN THINKING... YOU HAD SUCH GOOD LUCK RAISING AND SELLING YOUR RADISH...

MAYBE YOU SHOULD GO FOR THE BIG MONEY...

YES, THAT'S WHAT YOU SHOULD DO...

TRY TO RAISE A SOYBEAN!

THERE'S SOMEONE HERE FROM THE COUNTY TO SEE YOU...

IT'S ABOUT YOUR GARDEN.. I THINK THE FARMER NEXT DOOR CLAIMS YOU'RE USING PART OF HIS LAND

THAT'S RIDICULOUS!! WHAT DOES THIS GUY FROM THE COUNTY LOOK LIKE ANYWAY?

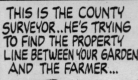

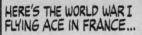

Panel 1: HERE'S THE WORLD WAR I FLYING ACE IN FRANCE...

Panel 2: BONJOUR, MONSIEUR... JE SUIS EN PANNE

Panel 3: OÙ EST LE GARAGE LE PLUS PROCHE?

Panel 4: I FALL IN LOVE WITH ANYONE WHO WILL TALK TO ME

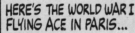

Panel 5: HERE'S THE WORLD WAR I FLYING ACE IN PARIS...

Panel 6: HE IS SITTING IN A SMALL SIDEWALK CAFE WITH A BEAUTIFUL YOUNG FRENCH LASS...

Panel 7: HE MUST IMPRESS HER WITH HIS SOPHISTICATED MANNER

Panel 8: MAY I SEE THE ROOT BEER LIST, PLEASE?

HERE'S THE WORLD WAR I FLYING ACE TAKING A BEAUTIFUL FRENCH LASS OUT TO DINNER...

POTAGE AU CERFEUIL... CANARD A L'ORANGE...

ESCARGOTS...FONDS D'ARTICHAUT...PÂTÉ DE FOIE GRAS...ET BEIGNETS, S'IL VOUS PLAÎT

UN ROOT BEER, S'IL VOUS PLAÎT

HERE'S THE WORLD WAR I FLYING ACE SAYING GOODBYE TO THE BEAUTIFUL FRENCH LASS BEFORE HE RETURNS TO THE FRONT...

SNIF!

NICE

QUICKLY HE SEARCHES THROUGH HIS PHRASE BOOK FOR THE WORDS THAT WILL EXPRESS WHAT IS IN HIS HEART...

RATS!

POW!

HEY, MANAGER, I'M WORKING ON A SPECIAL PROJECT

I'M TRYING TO WRITE AN ARTICLE ABOUT SOME OF THE FUNNY THINGS THAT HAPPEN IN BASEBALL GAMES...

IF YOU CAN THINK OF ANYTHING FUNNY, LET ME KNOW

I DOUBT THAT I'LL COME UP WITH A THING!

HELLO, SALLY? I JUST CALLED TO FIND OUT HOW YOUR BROTHER IS...

I SUPPOSE YOU THOUGHT I'D THINK YOU WERE CALLING TO ASK ME TO GO TO THE MOVIES!

WELL, I DIDN'T!! AND I WOULDN'T GO TO THE MOVIES WITH YOU NOW EVEN IF YOU ASKED ME, SO THERE!

WELL, HOW IS HE?

HOW IS WHO?

HOSPITAL ZONE QUIET!

EMERGENCY ENTRANCE

GOOD AFTERNOON, MA'AM! I DON'T MEAN TO BE ANY TROUBLE...

BUT I HAVE THE AWFUL FEELING THAT I MAY BE AN EMERGENCY!

SCHULZ

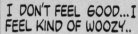

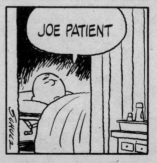

DID YOU HEAR THAT CHARLIE BROWN IS IN THE HOSPITAL?

HE IS?

WHAT'S THE FIRST THING YOU THINK WHEN YOU HEAR THAT A FRIEND HAS GONE TO THE HOSPITAL?

I'M GLAD IT WASN'T ME!

I HEARD THAT CHUCK'S IN THE HOSPITAL, SIR

I KNOW, MARCIE, AND I'M TRYING TO FIGURE OUT HOW I CAN SEND HIM SOME FLOWERS

THE EASIEST WAY, SIR, IS TO SEND THEM BY TELEPHONE...

SHE'S GOT TO BE KIDDING!

Dear Big Brother, I hope you are feeling better.

Things are fine here at home. I have moved into your room.

Don't worry about your personal things.

The flea market was a success.

I'M SO WORRIED ABOUT POOR CHARLIE BROWN LYING THERE IN THE HOSPITAL...

HE'S GOT TO GET WELL! HE'S GOT TO! OH, BOO HOO HOO HOO! SOB!

IT'S INTERESTING THAT YOU SHOULD CRY OVER HIM WHEN YOU'RE THE ONE WHO ALWAYS TREATED HIM SO MEAN!

AND STOP WIPING YOUR TEARS WITH MY PIANO!

WE CAN'T VISIT CHUCK BECAUSE WE'RE TOO YOUNG? RATS!

JUST FOR THAT WE'LL GO ACROSS THE STREET AND SIT ON A PARK BENCH AND STARE UP AT HIS ROOM!

IT'S A WELL-KNOWN FACT, MARCIE, THAT A PATIENT WILL RECOVER FASTER IF HE KNOWS A FRIEND IS STARING UP AT HIS ROOM...

YOU SHOULD HAVE BEEN A DOCTOR, SIR

THE LIGHT IN CHUCK'S ROOM JUST WENT OUT, MARCIE

HE'S PROBABLY GONE TO SLEEP, SIR

SLEEP WELL, CHUCK!

HOPE YOU FEEL BETTER IN THE MORNING!

WE MISS YOU, CHUCK!

WE LOVE YOU, CHUCK!

WE DO?

WE DO CHUCK'!!

YOUR OWNER'S STILL IN THE HOSPITAL SO I GUESS I HAVE TO FEED YOU

IF I CUT MY FINGER ON THE CAN OPENER, I'M GONNA SUE YOU!

WHO CARES?

A CASE LIKE THAT COULD DRAG ON FOR YEARS

I'M SO WORRIED ABOUT CHARLIE BROWN, I CAN'T EAT OR SLEEP...

WELL, IF YOU GET SICK, TOO, THAT SURE WON'T HELP HIM...

MAYBE IF HE THOUGHT HE WAS MAKING ME SICK, HE'D GET BETTER

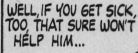

MAYBE I COULD SEND HIM A THREATENING LETTER

Dear Big Brother, How are things in the hospital? Things are fine at home.

I have been feeding your stupid dog every night even though he never thanks me.

SMAK!

Well, most of the time he doesn't.

SCHULZ

I JUST TALKED WITH CHARLIE BROWN'S MOM.. HE'S NOT ANY BETTER

HE'S NOT ANY BETTER? THAT'S CRAZY! HE'S GOT TO GET BETTER!!

WHAT'S WRONG WITH A WORLD WHERE SOMEONE LIKE CHARLIE BROWN CAN GET SICK, AND THEN NOT GET ANY BETTER?!

I NEED SOMEBODY TO HIT!!

SCHULZ

CHARLIE BROWN, I KNOW YOU CAN'T HEAR ME, BUT I WANT TO MAKE YOU A PROMISE...

IF YOU GET WELL, I PROMISE I'LL NEVER PULL THE FOOTBALL AWAY AGAIN!

THAT'S QUITE A PROMISE

I'LL BET HE FEELS BETTER ALREADY!

LET ME GET THIS STRAIGHT

IF CHARLIE BROWN GETS WELL, YOU PROMISE NEVER TO PULL THE FOOTBALL AWAY AGAIN?

THAT IS MY SOLEMN PROMISE!

HE'S SURE TO GET WELL NOW.. HE HAS SOMETHING TO LIVE FOR!

IF YOU SIT ON A PARK BENCH ACROSS FROM THE HOSPITAL AND STARE UP AT HIS WINDOW, THE PATIENT GETS BETTER...

POOR CHUCK..I HATE TO THINK OF HIM LYING UP THERE IN THAT HOSPITAL ROOM

YOU KIND OF LIKE CHUCK, DON'T YOU, SIR?

WELL, I..YOU KNOW... I FEEL SORT OF..YOU KNOW...HE..I...HE..

I LOVE CHUCK! I THINK HE'S REAL NEAT!

REAL NEAT? YOU THINK HE'S REAL NEAT?

I SURE DO! SOMEDAY I HOPE HE'LL ASK ME TO THE SENIOR PROM!

IN FACT, IF HE ASKED ME, I'D EVEN MARRY CHUCK!

COME WITH ME, MARCIE

IS THIS THE EMERGENCY ENTRANCE, MA'AM? WE'RE FRIENDS OF CHARLES BROWN

I HAVE ANOTHER PATIENT FOR YOU.. I THINK SHE'S SICKER THAN HE IS!

CHARLIE BROWN! YOU'RE BACK!! YOU'RE WELL!

I HEARD SOMETHING ABOUT A PROMISE..

OH, GOOD GRIEF!

YOU HOLD THE BALL, AND I'LL COME RUNNING UP AND KICK IT

REMEMBER, YOU PROMISED THAT IF I GOT WELL, YOU'D NEVER PULL THE FOOTBALL AWAY AGAIN

CAN'T I CHANGE MY MIND?

NO, YOU CAN'T BREAK A PROMISE TO A SICK FRIEND

HA! NOW, WHAT ARE YOU GONNA DO?

QUIET! I'M THINKING!

SCHULZ

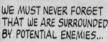

WE MUST NEVER FORGET THAT WE ARE SURROUNDED BY POTENTIAL ENEMIES...

I THINK WE SHOULD PRACTICE SOME DRILLS TO SEE HOW YOU REACT IN AN EMERGENCY...

BE READY, NOW... I'M GOING TO TRY TO CATCH YOU BY SURPRISE...

BEAR!

VERY GOOD! EXCELLENT REACTION!

SNAKE!

GOOD! QUICK MOVE!

BE READY.... BE ALERT...

CHICKEN HAWK!

WELL, THAT LAST ONE MAY NEED A LITTLE WORK..

SCHULZ

AS WE CROSS THE DESERT, I AM REMINDED OF A TRIVIA QUESTION

"BEAU GESTE" WAS FILMED THREE TIMES... WHO WERE THE ACTORS WHO PLAYED THE SERGEANT?

"NOAH BEERY, BRIAN DONLEVY AND TELLY SAVALAS"

RATS! HOW DID HE KNOW THAT?

ALL RIGHT, OLIVIER, YOU THINK YOU'RE SO GOOD AT MOVIE TRIVIA QUESTIONS...

IN THE 1926 VERSION OF "BEAU GESTE", RONALD COLMAN PLAYED BEAU... WHO PLAYED DIGBY AND WHO PLAYED JOHN?

"NEIL HAMILTON AND RALPH FORBES"

I THINK I'LL SIT DOWN, AND DRINK A GLASS OF SAND

"NEEDLES, CALIFORNIA..
A RECREATIONAL CENTER
ON THE COLORADO RIVER"

"ELEVATION, 463 FEET...
AVERAGE RAINFALL, FIVE
INCHES PER YEAR..."

"ATTRACTIONS IN THE
AREA ARE OLD GHOST
TOWNS AND TOPOCK SWAMP"

THAT MUST BE WHERE
MY BROTHER SPIKE
LIVES...TOPOCK SWAMP!

SPIKE!

WOOF!

MY BROTHER SPIKE!
WOW! IT'S GOOD TO
SEE YOU AGAIN!

SO THIS IS WHERE
YOU LIVE, HUH?
YOU'RE RIGHT, IT LOOKS A
LITTLE LIKE MY HOUSE

I'M GLAD OUR MOM
NEVER SAW THIS

SPIKE, YOU LOOK TERRIBLE...WHAT'S HAPPENED TO YOU?

MOM AND DAD DIDN'T RAISE YOU TO BE A DESERT RAT...YOU'RE WASTING YOUR LIFE...

IT'S NOT TOO LATE TO MAKE SOMETHING OF YOURSELF... COME HOME WITH ME..I'LL HELP YOU... WHAT DO YOU SAY?

SNIF

SCHULZ

WHY DO YOU WANT TO LIVE OUT HERE IN THE DESERT WITH THE SNAKES, AND THE LIZARDS AND THE COYOTES?

COME HOME WITH ME, SPIKE, AND LIVE A NORMAL LIFE...

OH, REALLY? WELL, I CAN UNDERSTAND THAT..

IT'S HARD TO LEAVE WHEN YOUR BOWLING TEAM IS IN FIRST PLACE...

SCHULZ

OKAY, MEN, BREAK OUT THE OL' SLEEPING BAGS...

CAN HE DO WHAT?

WHY, SURE! THAT WOULD BE GREAT

I HAD NO IDEA THAT CONRAD COULD PLAY TAPS...

WAIT UNTIL WE ALL GET SETTLED IN OUR SLEEPING BAGS...THEN GO RIGHT AHEAD

IT'S ALWAYS AN EMOTIONAL EXPERIENCE TO HEAR TAPS PLAYED JUST BEFORE YOU GO TO SLEEP...

TAP TAP TAP TAP TAP

I CAN'T STAND IT..

HEE HEE HEE HEE

COME IN! COME IN! SIT ANYWHERE!

GOOD EVENING, SIR.. WELCOME TO THE FANCIEST RESTAURANT IN TOWN!

OUR SPECIAL TONIGHT IS DOG FOOD... IT IS SCOOPED CAREFULLY FROM THE CAN, PLOPPED LIGHTLY INTO THE DISH AND STIRRED VIGOROUSLY INTO AN APPETIZING DELIGHT...

YOU'LL HAVE THE SPECIAL THEN, SIR? GOOD! YOU'LL NOT BE SORRY!

WOULD YOU CARE FOR A DRINK BEFORE DINNER? A BOWL OF WATER PERHAPS? FINE!

YOUR WAITER WILL BE WITH YOU IN A MOMENT...

IF THIS IS SUCH A FANCY PLACE, WHY THE PAPER NAPKIN?

SCHULZ

KAMP OUTT

THAT WASN'T A BAD BREAKFAST

ANY BREAKFAST IS GOOD WHEN YOU'RE STARVING TO DEATH

DO YOU ALWAYS BRING YOUR BROTHER'S DOG TO CAMP?

NO, BUT I THOUGHT HE MIGHT ENJOY IT...

IF I THROW THIS STICK INTO THE WATER, WILL HE SWIM OUT AND BRING IT BACK?

HERE, DOGGIE.. SEE THE NICE STICK?

"DOGGIE"?

GO GET IT!

WHERE'D HE GO?

HE'S COMING..

SCHULZ

EVERYONE IS COMPLAINING ABOUT THE HEAT, CHARLIE BROWN...

I KNOW...I HAVE TO ADMIT IT'S PRETTY WARM FOR PLAYING BASEBALL

THE ONLY ONE WHO HASN'T COMPLAINED IS LUCY...

NEXT YEAR I'M GONNA BE A FREE AGENT

YOU ARE, HUH?

DO YOU KNOW WHAT A FREE AGENT IS?

NOPE

BUT I'M GONNA BE ONE!!

HEY, CATCHER!

IT'S LONELY OUT THERE IN RIGHT FIELD SO I'M GONNA STAND HERE WITH YOU

IF YOU STAND THERE, YOU'LL GET HIT BY A FOUL BALL

HOW ABOUT HERE?

THIS IS THE LAST GAME OF THE SEASON, MANAGER...

LET'S PLAY OUR HEARTS OUT!

I KNOW HOW THAT WORKS...

YOU PLAY YOUR HEART OUT, AND YOU GET A STOMACHACHE!

DISTANCES ON A BASEBALL DIAMOND ARE DECEIVING...

WHEN YOU WALK FROM THE BENCH TO THE PLATE, IT'S ABOUT THIRTY FEET...

STRIKE THREE!

WHEN YOU WALK FROM THE PLATE TO THE BENCH, IT'S FOUR MILES!

POW!

WELL, THAT DOES IT FOR ANOTHER SEASON, MANAGER! NOW, YOU HAVE TWO CHOICES..

YOU CAN GO HOME AND BROOD ABOUT THIS SEASON ALL WINTER LONG, OR YOU CAN LIE HERE AND ROT!

THOSE ARE GREAT CHOICES

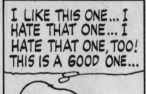

A BEAN BAG IS A PERFECT PLACE TO SULK

YOU CAN SINK WAY DOWN DEEP, AND SULK FOR HOURS...

YOU ONLY HAVE TO STICK YOUR HEAD UP ONCE IN A WHILE...

...TO SEE IF ANYBODY CARES

SULKING IN YOUR BEAN BAG, I SEE...

GO AWAY, AND LEAVE ME ALONE!

TELL ME SOMETHING.. WHAT DO YOU DO WITH A BEAN BAG IF YOU LIE IN IT ALL DAY, AND YOU STILL FEEL CRABBY?

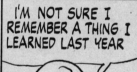

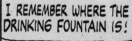

YOU'LL NEVER GET GOOD GRADES, MARCIE, IF YOU CHANGE SEATS ALL THE TIME!

REPEAT THE QUESTION, WILL YOU, MA'AM? THERE'S AN ECHO DOWN HERE...

I'VE GOT IT!

YES, MA'AM, I THINK I KNOW THE ANSWER

SIXTEEN..FOUR.. THIRTY-SEVEN

ON SECOND THOUGHT, THAT MAY BE MY LOCKER COMBINATION!

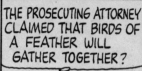

WELL, HOW DID THE TRIAL TURN OUT?

THE PROSECUTING ATTORNEY CLAIMED THAT BIRDS OF A FEATHER WILL GATHER TOGETHER?

BUT THE DEFENSE ATTORNEY SAID THAT A BIRD IN THE HAND IS WORTH TWO IN THE BUSH...

YOU'RE RIGHT...A VERY DIFFICULT CASE

I'VE BECOME INTERESTED IN LEARNING ABOUT THE EARTH'S SURFACE

FOR INSTANCE, HAVE YOU EVER NOTICED THIS LAVA FORMATION?

ANCIENT LAVA FLOWS SUCH AS THIS ONE HERE ARE REALLY QUITE FASCINATING

I ALWAYS THOUGHT THIS WAS OUR DRIVEWAY!

boot!

BONK!

EXPLAIN TITLE IX TO ME AGAIN, WILL YOU?

THAT'S A NICE FOOTBALL YOU HAVE THERE, LINUS

SHALL I GIVE HIM THE STATISTICS, SIR?

IN 1978, THE AVERAGE BUDGET FOR INTERCOLLEGIATE ATHLETICS FOR MEN WAS $717,000, BUT FOR WOMEN IT WAS ONLY $141,000

SIGH

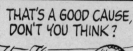

IF YOU DON'T HELP ME WORK FOR WOMEN IN SPORTS, MARCIE, I'LL NEVER INTRODUCE YOU TO BILLIE JEAN KING!

YOU DON'T EVEN KNOW BILLIE JEAN KING, SIR

HOW CAN YOU SAY, "BILLIE JEAN KING, MAY I PRESENT MARCIE?" WHEN YOU DON'T KNOW BILLIE JEAN KING?

ASK HER A HARD QUESTION, MA'AM! SHE'S DRIVING ME CRAZY!

YOU'RE SURE YOU'RE NOT INTERESTED IN WOMEN'S SPORTS, MARCIE?

NOPE! AS A MATTER OF FACT, I'M GOING TO START TAKING ORGAN LESSONS FROM MRS. HAGEMEYER

YOU'RE A BIG DISAPPOINTMENT TO ME, MARCIE...

I'LL SEND YOU TICKETS TO MY FIRST RECITAL, SIR

I SUPPOSE YOU THINK YOU'RE FUNNY!

I'VE BEEN THINKING ABOUT US...

YOU KNOW...YOU AND ME...

I SUPPOSE THERE COMES A TIME WHEN MOST RELATIONSHIPS SIMPLY COME TO AN END...MAYBE THAT'S HAPPENED TO US...

I GUESS IT WILL BE BETTER ALL AROUND IF WE JUST PART SORT OF FRIENDLY AND ADMIT THAT THE LOVE WE ONCE HAD IS NOW GONE...

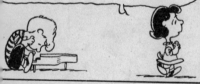

THESE THINGS HAPPEN EVERY DAY... I GUESS WE JUST THINK IT'LL NEVER HAPPEN TO US, BUT IT DID...WE HAD OUR LOVE, BUT NOW IT'S GONE!

HA HA HA HA! BOY, I REALLY HAD YOU FOOLED, DIDN'T I? I REALLY HAD YOU WORRIED! HA HA HA HA! I'M SORRY IF I UPSET YOU..I REALLY HAD YOU GOING, DIDN'T I? HA HA HA HA! I HAD NO IDEA YOU'D GET SO UPSET...

RATS!

SCHULZ

MA'AM?

NO, MA'AM, I DON'T KNOW THE LOCATION OF SVALBARD...

BUT I KNOW A GREAT RECIPE FOR NOODLES WITH SOUR CREAM...

EVERYTHING I KNOW I KNOW AT THE WRONG TIME!

HERE, I BOUGHT YOU A NEW BOOK

HOW THOUGHTFUL!

THIS IS ONE I HADN'T HEARD OF

"THE HOUND OF THE BEAGLEVILLES"

TRUE? WHO KNOWS? FALSE? ONLY TIME WILL TELL...

PERHAPS... COULD BE... MAYBE..I DOUBT IT... DON'T COUNT ON IT...

MAYBE IN THE LONG RUN...IT ALL DEPENDS... WEATHER PERMITTING

SOME OF US, MA'AM, SEE EVERYTHING IN SHADES OF GRAY

WHAT DO FARMERS DO IN THE WINTER?

WELL, IN THE OLD DAYS THEY USED TO MEND THEIR HARNESS

I DON'T KNOW WHAT THEY DO NOWADAYS

MAYBE THEY JOIN A BOWLING LEAGUE!

I DON'T KNOW WHY I ACCEPT WOODSTOCK'S STUPID BREAKFAST INVITATIONS

WELL, I'M HERE! WHAT ARE WE HAVING?

I KNEW IT! ONE CROUTON WITH GRAPE JELLY!

RATS!

HE WHO LIVES BY THE DIRTY ROTTEN LITTLE DROP SHOT, DIES BY THE DIRTY ROTTEN LITTLE DROP SHOT!

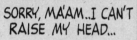
SORRY, MA'AM..I CAN'T RAISE MY HEAD...

MAYBE IF YOU WALKED AROUND TO THE SIDE OF THE ROOM AND STOOD THERE JUST A LITTLE TO THE LEFT OF THE RADIATOR..

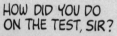
HOW DID YOU DO ON THE TEST, SIR?

I GOT TWO RIGHT OUT OF TWENTY

THAT WASN'T VERY GOOD, SIR...

FROM ALL I'VE HEARD, MARCIE, IT'S LONELY AT THE TOP!

WHO, ME?

WHOM, I?

YES, MA'AM..I HAVE MY REPORT READY

THIS IS THE CLASSIC STORY OF PETER RABBIT AND HIS COAT OF MANY COLORS

HIS BROTHERS HATED HIM SO WHEN HE LOST HIS COAT OF MANY COLORS WHILE CLIMBING OVER THE FARMER'S FENCE, THEY SOLD HIM TO THE PHARAOH IN EGYPT!

THIS IS A STORY OF JEALOUSY, DESIRE AND FORGIVENESS, AND SHOULD BE A LESSON TO US ALL!

THANK YOU

PSST! WHY DID THE TEACHER HAVE SUCH A FUNNY LOOK ON HER FACE?

MAYBE SHE DOESN'T FEEL WELL

WAIT UNTIL TOMORROW WHEN I RECITE ANOTHER CLASSIC, "THE OWL AND THE FUSSY CAT"

WOMEN SHOULDN'T BE THE ONLY ONES TO CRY

MEN SHOULD REALIZE THAT IT'S ALL RIGHT FOR THEM TO CRY, TOO...

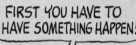

FIRST YOU HAVE TO HAVE SOMETHING HAPPEN!

I CAN UNDERSTAND WHY SOME PEOPLE LIKE TO LIVE BY THE OCEAN

THE SOUND OF THE WAVES AT NIGHT CAN BE VERY SOOTHING

THE SAME SORT OF THING SOMETIMES HELPS ME...

I'M LULLED TO SLEEP BY THE SOUND OF THE WAVES LAPPING AGAINST THE SIDE OF MY WATER DISH

SCHULZ

I'VE BEEN GOING OVER OUR STATISTICS FOR THIS PAST BASEBALL SEASON

YOUR FIELDING WASN'T VERY GOOD, LUCY

YOU DIDN'T CATCH ONE BALL DURING THE ENTIRE SEASON

DANDELIONS GOT IN MY EYES!

WE'RE SUPPOSED TO DO A REPORT ON PRAIRIE DOGS

WHAT DO I KNOW ABOUT PRAIRIE DOGS? I'VE NEVER EVEN SEEN ONE

BESIDES, WE DON'T LIVE ON A PRAIRIE

HOW ABOUT A VACANT LOT DOG?

BONK!

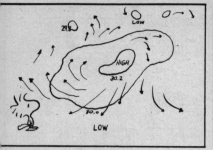

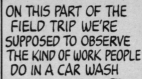

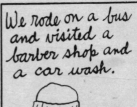

MA'AM, HAVE YOU EVER NOTICED HOW THE ATMOSPHERE IN OUR ROOM CHANGES WHEN IT'S RAINING OUTSIDE?

WITH THE LIGHTS ON IN HERE, AND THE RAIN AND DARKNESS OUTSIDE, THERE'S SORT OF A MEDIEVAL ATMOSPHERE...

NO, MA'AM, I DON'T KNOW WHAT THE CAPITAL OF NORWAY IS...

SO MUCH FOR ATMOSPHERE

MA'AM, I THINK THE CEILING IS LEAKING...

YES, MA'AM, RIGHT UP THERE... SEE?

I TOLD HER ABOUT IT, SIR

THANKS, MARCIE.. I DON'T LIKE TO BE THE KIND WHO COMPLAINS

YES, MA'AM, I GUESS THAT WORKS...

THANK YOU FOR TELLING THE CUSTODIAN ABOUT THE LEAK IN THE CEILING, MA'AM...

HE CERTAINLY TOOK CARE OF IT FAST, DIDN'T HE, SIR?

YOU MIGHT SAY THAT..

GUESS WHAT, SIR..

I HEARD THAT THE BOARD OF EDUCATION AND THE PRINCIPAL HAVE BEEN ARGUING ABOUT THE LEAK IN THE CEILING...

THEY CAN'T DECIDE WHAT TO DO...I IMAGINE IT'S A FINANCIAL PROBLEM, WOULDN'T YOU SAY, SIR?

JUST EMPTY THE PAN AGAIN WILL YOU, MARCIE?

THE PRINCIPAL TOLD THE TEACHER SHE MIGHT CONSIDER MOVING YOU TO ANOTHER DESK, SIR

BUT SHE SAID SHE CAN'T DO THAT

WHY NOT?

SHE SAID IT WOULD DESTROY HER ALPHABETICAL SEATING ARRANGEMENT

I THINK IT'S STOPPED RAINING, SIR

YOU CAN TAKE THE PAN OFF YOUR HEAD NOW

MAYBE YOU COULD GIVE OUR CLASS A REPORT ON THE ANNUAL RAINFALL IN THIS AREA...

I THINK I'VE DISCOVERED SOMETHING

WHEN YOU WAKE UP AT NIGHT, AND YOUR HEAD HURTS AND YOUR STOMACH FEELS FUNNY...

THE FIRST THING YOU DO IS PUT ON YOUR BATHROBE

THEN YOU DRINK A GLASS OF WATER AND TAKE SOME PILLS, AND YOU SIT BY YOURSELF IN THE DARK FOR A WHILE UNTIL YOU'RE READY TO GO BACK TO BED...

BUT IT'S NOT THE PILLS THAT MADE YOU FEEL BETTER..

IT'S THE BATHROBE!

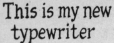
This is my new
typewriter

It has many
typefaces.

IT CAN ALSO
cross out
mistakes.

WHAT ARE YOU
DOING, SIR?

QUIET, MARCIE...I'M
TRYING TO MAKE THE
TEACHER BELIEVE
I'M THINKING...

IF SHE BELIEVES THAT,
SHE'LL BELIEVE ANYTHING

SARCASM, MARCIE, WILL
TURN YOUR TONGUE INTO
A CARROT STICK!

..MIX TOGETHER AND ADD SLOWLY ONE CUP SELF RISING FLOUR TO MIX ...

DO NOT MAKE BATTER TOO SOFT..IT MUST DROP FROM A TABLESPOON INTO HOT FAT ABOUT ONE INCH DEEP IN FRYING PAN...

HOW CAN YOU THINK ZUCCHINI FRITTERS AND STILL GET DOG FOOD?

Dear Santa Claus, How have you been?

I FEEL LIKE AN IDIOT WRITING TO SOMEONE WHO DOESN'T EXIST

ON THE OTHER HAND, IF HE REALLY DOES EXIST AND I DON'T WRITE, I'D FEEL EVEN DUMBER!

THIS IS THE TIME OF YEAR WHEN IT'S BEST TO TOUCH ALL BASES

WHATEVER THAT MEANS

MA'AM?

NO, I DON'T HAVE ANY IDEA

I'M AFRAID MY BRAIN HAS LEFT FOR THE DAY

WOULD YOU CARE TO LEAVE A MESSAGE WITH THE ANSWERING SERVICE?

"AND THERE WERE IN THE SAME COUNTRY SHEPHERDS ABIDING IN THE FIELDS"

THIS OTHER TRANSLATION SAYS, "THAT NIGHT SOME SHEPHERDS WERE IN THE FIELD"

I THINK I LIKE "ABIDING" BETTER

SO DO I... ABSOLUTELY! MUCH BETTER!

WHAT DOES "ABIDING" MEAN?

LUCY GAVE ME HER CHRISTMAS LIST, BUT I CAN'T REMEMBER WHERE I PUT IT...

I'VE GOT TO FIND THAT LIST...

I CAN'T IMAGINE WHERE IT COULD BE..

IF I DIDN'T HAVE TENURE, I THINK MAYBE I'D MOVE

I'VE MADE UP A NEW LIST OF THINGS I WANT FOR CHRISTMAS, CHARLIE BROWN

I HATE TO ADMIT IT, BUT I CAN'T EVEN REMEMBER WHERE WE PUT THE OTHER LIST

DON'T WORRY, I KNOW JUST WHERE IT IS...

JOE SPINDLE!

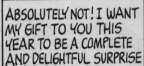

THOSE ARE NICE MITTENS.. BE CAREFUL NOT TO LOSE THEM, OR YOU WON'T GET ANY PIE!

THE THREE LITTLE KITTENS!

HAVEN'T YOU EVER HEARD OF THE THREE LITTLE KITTENS? GOOD GRIEF!

LITERARY REFERENCES ARE WASTED ON WOODSTOCK...

I GUESS WE ALL DO SOME DUMB THINGS AND WE ALL DO SOME SMART THINGS

MY GRANDFATHER SAYS THE DUMBEST THING HE EVER DID WAS NOT FINISH HIGH SCHOOL

WHAT WAS THE SMARTEST THING?

HE NEVER BOUGHT A NEHRU JACKET!

YES, MA'AM?

WHAT WAS THE NAME OF THE KING WHOSE DAUGHTER'S MARRIAGE MADE POSSIBLE THE UNIFICATION OF DENMARK AND NORWAY IN 1380?

WOW! THAT'S THE KIND OF QUESTION THAT MAKES YOUR TEMPLES THROB..

IT MAKES YOUR EARS RING AND YOUR HAIR STAND ON END...

IT MAKES YOUR EYES WATER, YOUR CHEEKS BURN, YOUR MOUTH TURN DRY AND YOUR TEETH ACHE...

A QUESTION LIKE THAT CAN DESTROY YOUR WHOLE HEAD!

POW!

I DID IT! I DID IT! I CONFESS! I DID IT!

OH, I FEEL SO GUILTY! I DON'T KNOW WHAT CAME OVER ME! I FEEL SO GUILTY!

HOLD ON! YOU CAN'T GET AWAY WITH THAT!

ALL RIGHT, WHO THREW THAT SNOWBALL? COME OUT, WHEREVER YOU ARE!

NOW, YOU WERE SAYING...

WELL, I... I...I...I DID IT, I GUESS, AND...

WHOP!!

EVERYTHING IN ITS PROPER ORDER

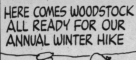

HERE COMES WOODSTOCK ALL READY FOR OUR ANNUAL WINTER HIKE

HEY! THAT'S A GREAT FUR HAT!

IT'S GOING TO BE COLD TODAY..MAYBE YOU SHOULD PULL THE EARFLAPS DOWN

NO, I GUESS NOT

THOSE ARE GREAT HATS YOU GUYS ARE WEARING

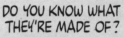

DO YOU KNOW WHAT THEY'RE MADE OF?

HONK HONK

BAA!

GOOSE DOWN AND LAMB FUR..HOW NICE

LOOK, MEN, IT'S BEGINNING TO SNOW

WHEN YOU'RE ON A HIKE LIKE THIS AND IT STARTS TO SNOW, IT'S IMPORTANT TO KEEP MOVING...

WHY?

THAT'S WHY!

!?∞∞X!!

EVERY TIME WE GO ON A HIKE WE GET LOST... IS THAT A HOUSE? I THINK I SEE A HOUSE...

GET UP THERE, OLIVIER, AND LOOK IN THE WINDOW..IS ANYONE HOME? WHAT DO YOU SEE?

YOU'RE KIDDING.. LET ME LOOK

DON'T FUSS, MEN, WE'RE ALL IN THIS TOGETHER

∞∞∞ XXX !!!!

ELVES! THE PLACE IS FULL OF ELVES!

AND THERE'S A FAT GUY IN THERE WITH A RED SUIT

LET ME DOWN, MEN, I'VE GOT A GREAT IDEA...

THAT WASN'T IT!

I KNEW IT! I KNEW THERE'D BE A SLEIGH AROUND HERE SOMEWHERE

THIS FAT GUY IN THE RED SUIT FLIES ALL OVER THE WORLD...

ALL WE HAVE TO DO IS HITCH A RIDE ON THE BACK, AND WE'LL BE HOME IN NO TIME...

NO, OLIVIER, THEY PROBABLY WON'T SHOW A MOVIE ON THIS FLIGHT

MUSTN'T TOUCH!!

A PACKAGE JUST CAME FOR YOU, BUT IT SAYS, "DO NOT OPEN UNTIL CHRISTMAS"

DOGS CAN'T READ! HEE HEE HEE!!

HOW NICE! A NEW STOCKING CAP

HE WAS RIGHT.. I SHOULD HAVE WAITED...

NOW, EVERYONE ELSE WILL BE OPENING PRESENTS, BUT I'LL JUST HAVE TO STAND AROUND AND WATCH! RATS!

I'M SO STUPID!

I DO THIS EVERY YEAR

SURPRISE! ANOTHER PACKAGE JUST CAME, BUT IT SAYS, "DO NOT OPEN UNTIL.."

WHO CARES?

I CAN'T WAIT! I CAN'T WAIT!

I'M SO STUPID!

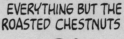

WE HAD A TRADITIONAL CHRISTMAS THIS YEAR

EVERYTHING BUT THE ROASTED CHESTNUTS

THAT WASN'T TRADITIONAL?

NOT IN A MICROWAVE OVEN!

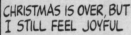

CHRISTMAS IS OVER, BUT I STILL FEEL JOYFUL

I THINK I'M GOING TO BE ABLE TO KEEP THIS GOOD FEELING ABOUT MYSELF AND EVERYONE FOR A REAL LONG TIME...

WHO CARES?

AND A HAPPY NEW YEAR TO YOU, TOO!

1980

BOOGIE DOWN!

WHOOPIE!! BRING ON THE ROOT BEER! BRING ON THE DANCING BEAGLETTES!

NO DANCING BEAGLETTES? YOU'RE KIDDING!

HOW CAN YOU HAVE A NEW YEAR'S PARTY WITHOUT DANCING BEAGLETTES?!

WHAT A STUPID PARTY! I'M GOING HOME!

NO DANCING BEAGLETTES...I CAN'T BELIEVE IT...

APOLOGIZE? NO, YOU DON'T HAVE TO APOLOGIZE

IT WASN'T YOUR FAULT... I SHOULDN'T ALWAYS GET SO UPSET...DON'T APOLOGIZE

HAPPY NEW YEAR, OLD FRIEND! HAPPY NEW YEAR!

NO DANCING BEAGLETTES... ✳ SIGH ✳

YOU DON'T HAVE ANY SHIN PADS?

YOU CAN'T PLAY HOCKEY WITHOUT SHIN PADS...

I WONDER IF A COUPLE OF MAGAZINES WOULD WORK...

NO, I GUESS NOT

THAT STUPID WOODSTOCK!

HE COST US THE HOCKEY GAME...

HE TRIED TO USE MAGAZINES FOR SHIN PADS...SO WHAT HAPPENED?

THE OTHER TEAM SCORED WHILE HE WAS READING HIS SHIN PADS!

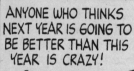

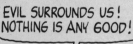

CHARLIE BROWN, DO YOU THINK I WASN'T INVITED TO A NEW YEAR'S PARTY BECAUSE I'M TOO CRABBY?

NO, YOU WERE PROBABLY INVITED TO NINE PARTIES, BUT ALL THE INVITATIONS WERE LOST IN THE MAIL

THAT NEVER OCCURRED TO ME..I'LL BET THAT'S JUST WHAT HAPPENED

SOMEDAY YOU'RE GOING TO LOOK AT ME LIKE THAT, AND YOUR EYES ARE GONNA STICK!

DID I SEE YOUR FAMILY TAKING DOWN YOUR CHRISTMAS TREE YESTERDAY?

ALL THE DECORATIONS AND ORNAMENTS HAVE BEEN PACKED AWAY, AND EVERYTHING CLEANED UP

HOW ABOUT YOU?

I HAVEN'T SENT OUT MY CARDS YET!

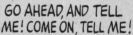

OUR TEACHER SAYS WE HAVE TO MEASURE SOMETHING WITH A RULER

HOLD STILL...I'LL TRY MEASURING YOUR MOUTH AGAIN...

HMM...ONE LIP IS ON THE SIX AND THE OTHER LIP IS ON THE NINE...

I WONDER HOW YOU WRITE THAT... I'LL PUT, "LIP TO LIP, THREE INCHES"

I CAN'T STAND IT!

RULERS HAVE OTHER USES, YOU KNOW

SEE? IF YOU TAKE YOUR PEN AND GO ALONG THE EDGE OF THE RULER, AND THEN LIFT IT UP, YOU'LL HAVE A NICE STRAIGHT...

...SMUDGE!